Tell the Time

How to use this book with your child:

It is recommended that an adult spends time with a child while doing any kind of homework, to offer encouragement and guidance. Find a quiet place to work, preferably at a table, and encourage your child to hold his or her pen or pencil correctly.

Try to work at your child's pace and avoid spending too long on any one page or activity. Most of all, emphasise the fun element of what you are doing and enjoy this special and exciting time!

Don't forget to add a reward sticker to each page you complete!

Reward
sticker!

Designed by Plum5
Illustrations by Sue King, Sharon Smart and Andy Geeson
Educational consultant Chris Andrew and Nina Filipek

 AUTUMN PUBLISHING

Before or after?

Read the questions below and label each picture with either **before** or **after**.

a. Do you turn a tap on **before** or **after** you wash your hands?

```
┌─────────────────────────────┐
│                             │
│                             │
└─────────────────────────────┘
```

b. Are you likely to wash the dishes **before** or **after** a meal?

```
┌─────────────────────────────┐
│                             │
│                             │
└─────────────────────────────┘
```

Reward
sticker!

c. Do you put a lead on a dog **before** or **after** you take it for a walk?

d. Do you cheer **before** or **after** someone scores a goal?

Reward sticker!

How long?

Time is measured in **seconds**, **minutes** and **hours**.

There are 60 **seconds** in one **minute**.

There are 60 **minutes** in one **hour**.

a. How long does it take to pick up a pen?
Circle the correct answer.

3 seconds   **3 minutes**   **3 hours**

Reward
sticker!

b. How long does it take to brush your teeth?
Circle the correct answer.

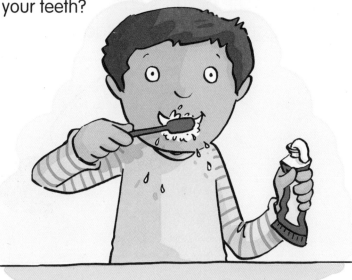

2 seconds   **2 minutes**   **2 hours**

c. How long does it take to watch a film?
Circle the correct answer.

2 seconds   **2 minutes**   **2 hours**

Reward
sticker!

Longest time

Look at these pictures carefully. Which do you think takes the longest amount of time? Place a ✔ in the box.

a.

doing a somersault ☐

climbing a mountain ☐

Reward sticker!

Which do you think takes the longest amount of time? Place a ✔ in the box.

b.

feeding the cat ☐

tidying your room ☐

Reward
sticker!

Day and night

Compare the pictures below. Can you work out which scene is **day** and which is **night** by looking at the differences between the pictures? Write the correct answers in the boxes.

a.

b.

Now, compare these pictures. Which picture is **day** and which is **night**? Write the correct answers in the boxes.

a.

b.

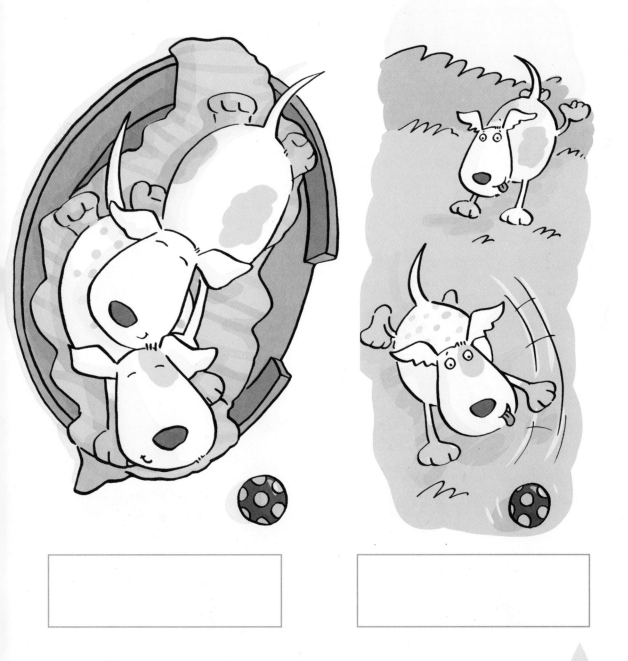

Clock face

There are 12 numbers on a clock face. Use the numbers on this page to help you label the clock on the opposite page. Write the numbers in the right squares. One has been done for you.

Reward sticker!

Clock hands

The hands on a clock face show you the time by pointing to numbers. The **short** hand points to the **hour** and the **long** hand points to the **minutes**.

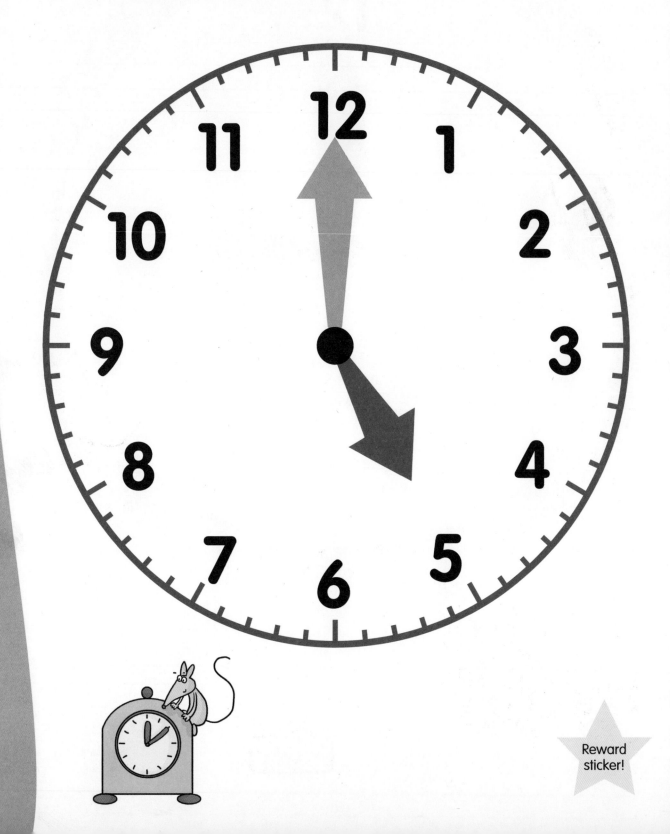

Reward sticker!

Using a ruler, draw the short hand and point it to the number 9.
Then, draw the long hand and point it to the number 12.
This shows you that it is 9 o'clock.

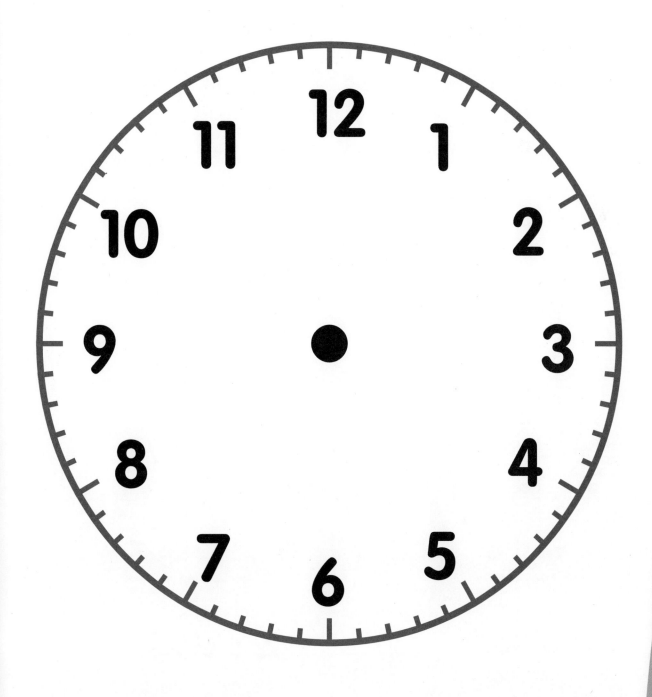

Reward sticker!

Practice 1

Look at the times in the boxes under each of these clocks. Draw hands on the clock faces so that they tell the times given in the boxes. Use the example to help you.

E.g.

| 1 o'clock |

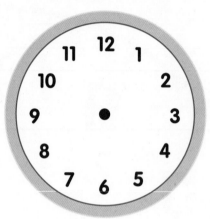

| 5 o'clock |

| 8 o'clock |

| 12 o'clock |

Reward
sticker!

2 o'clock

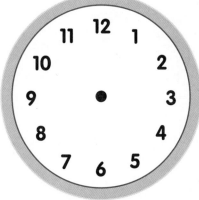

6 o'clock

4 o'clock

7 o'clock

10 o'clock

What time of day?

Use the clues in the pictures to help you decide when these events most likely took place. Choose from the words on the opposite page and write the correct word in the boxes.

a.

b.

morning   evening

afternoon   night-time

c.

d.

Reward sticker!

Adding by 5 minutes

To count the number of minutes in an hour, go around the clock face and keep adding fives until you reach 60. Finish writing the answers in the boxes.

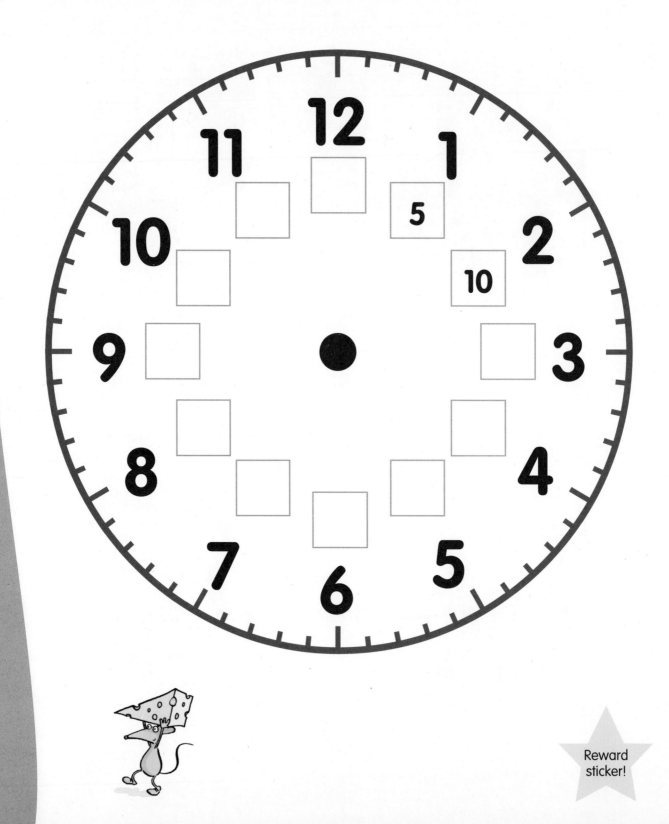

What's the time?

Match the times shown on the clocks to the correct time in the boxes, by drawing a line between them.

a.

b.

c.

d.

| 12 o'clock |

| 5 o'clock |

| 7 o'clock |

| 8 o'clock |

Reward sticker!

Half an hour

A clock face can be divided into two halves.
There are **30 minutes** in half an hour.

2 halves

half an hour
(30 minutes)

Reward
sticker!

Quarter of an hour

A clock face can also be divided into four quarters.
There are **15 minutes** in a quarter of an hour.

4 quarters

**quarter of an hour
(15 minutes)**

Half past

When the long hand points to the number 6, it is half past the hour.
Draw the long hand pointing to 6.
Then, draw the short hand pointing halfway between 2 and 3.
This shows that it is half past 2.

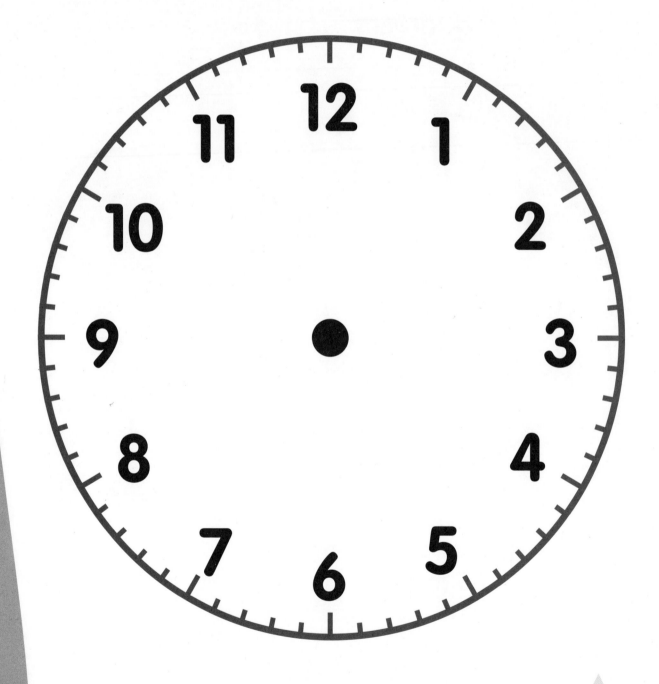

Reward sticker!

Quarter past

When the long hand points to the number 3, it is quarter past the hour. Draw the long hand pointing to 3.
Then, draw the short hand pointing to just past 10.
This shows that it is quarter past 10.

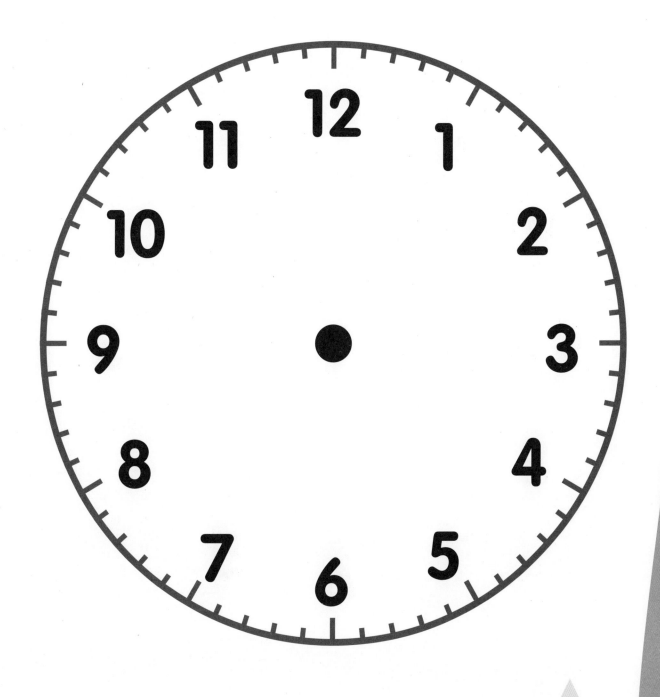

Reward sticker!

Quarter to

When the long hand points to the number 9, it is quarter to the hour. Draw the long hand pointing to 9.
Then, draw the short hand pointing almost to 5.
This shows that it is quarter to 5.

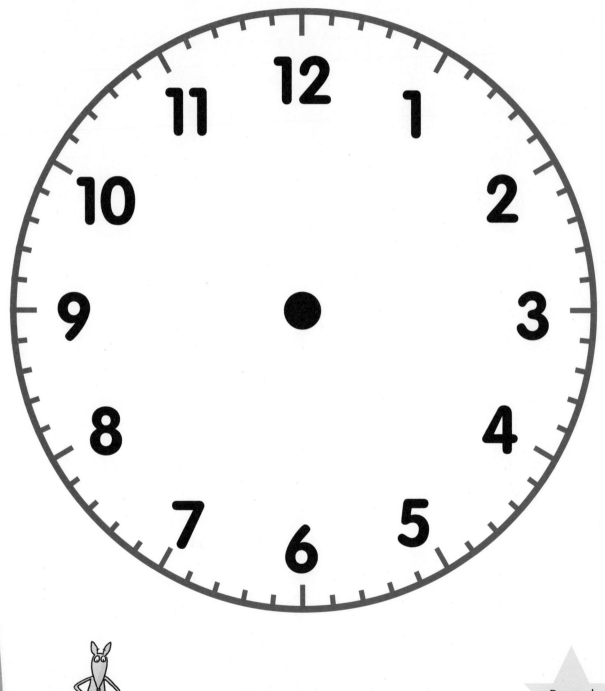

Reward
sticker!

Practice 2

Look at the times on these clocks. Match the times on the clocks to the correct time in the boxes, by drawing a line between them.

a.

b.
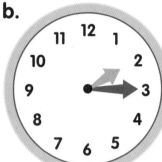

c.
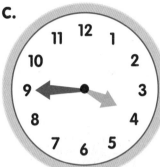

quarter to 4	half past 3	quarter past 2

Look at the times in the boxes.
Draw the missing hands on the faces below.

d.
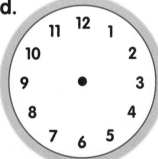

e.

f.

half past 6	quarter past 8	quarter to 10

What time?

Look at these pictures. What time of day do you think each of the activities are taking place?
Draw the missing hands on the clock faces.

Reward sticker!

Reward sticker!

Draw the hands

Look at the times in the boxes, then draw the missing hands on the clock faces.

a.

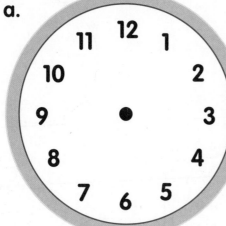

half past 2

b.

quarter to 8

c.

quarter past 7

d.

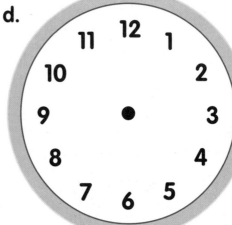

9 o'clock

Reward sticker!

e.
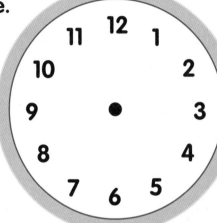

quarter to 3

f.
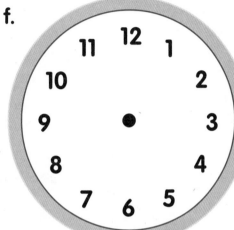

half past 10

g.
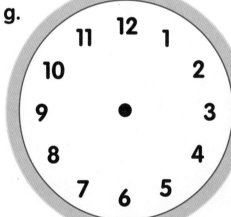

quarter past 11

h.
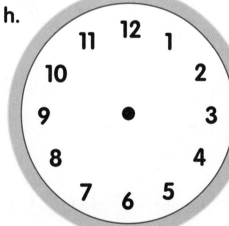

5 o'clock

Reward sticker!

24-hour clock

You have learnt that the hands on a 12-hour clock move around the clock face. After 12 o'clock midday, instead of starting again with 1 o'clock in the afternoon, a 24-hour clock shows 13:00.

2 o'clock in the afternoon is shown as 14:00, and so on.

The numbers change every minute up to 23:59 (1 minute before midnight). At midnight, a 24-hour clock shows 00:00, then starts again at 00:01 (1 minute past midnight).

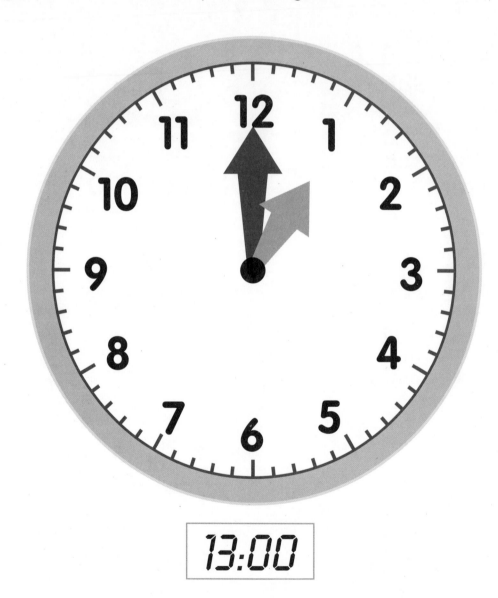

13:00

Reward sticker!

Practice 3

Look at the times on these 12-hour clock faces and match them to the same time on the 24-hour clocks below.

a.

b.

c.

14:00

15:00

13:00

Look at the times on these 24-hour clocks and draw the missing hands on the 12-hour clock faces, so they show the same time.

d.

e.
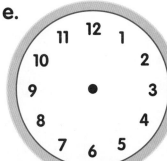

f.

16:00

17:00

18:00

Reward sticker!

Answers:

Pages 2-3: Before or after?
a. before **b.** after **c.** before **d.** after

Pages 4-5: How long?
a. 3 seconds **b.** 2 minutes **c.** 2 hours

Pages 6-7: Longest time
a. Climbing a mountain takes the longest time.
b. Tidying your room takes the longest time.

Pages 8-9: Day and night
a. day **b.** night   **a.** night **b.** day

Page 13: Clock hands

Pages 14-15: Practice 1

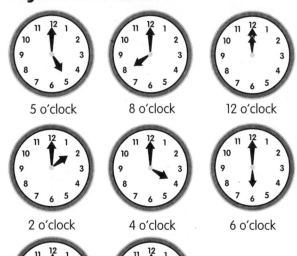

5 o'clock   8 o'clock   12 o'clock

2 o'clock   4 o'clock   6 o'clock

7 o'clock   10 o'clock

Pages 16-17: What time of day?
a. morning **b.** evening **c.** night-time **d.** afternoon

Page 19: What's the time?
a. 8 o'clock **b.** 12 o'clock **c.** 5 o'clock
d. 7 o'clock

Page 22: Half past	Page 23: Quarter past	Page 24: Quarter to

Page 25: Practice 2
a. half past 3 **b.** quarter past 2 **c.** quarter to four

half past 6   quarter past 8   quarter to 10

Pages 28-29: Draw the hands

a.   **b.**   **c.**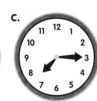

half past 2   quarter to 8   quarter past 7

d.   **e.**   **f.**

9 o'clock   quarter to 3   half past 10

g.   **h.**

quarter past 11   5 o'clock

Page 31: Practice 3
a. 13:00 **b.** 14:00 **c.** 15:00

d.  **e.**   **f.**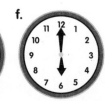